He can run.

She can run.

He can swing.

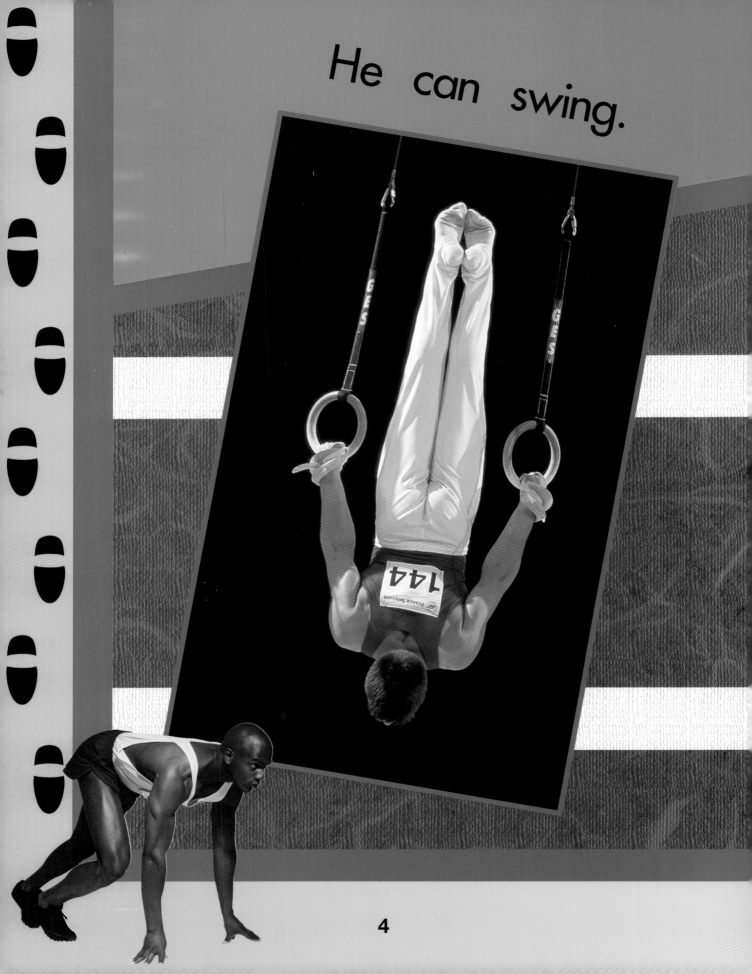

Run and Swing and Jump

Written by Harry Chan

ISBN: 1572559640

Contents

Special Features

Page 2
Run and Swing and Jump

Page 12
Follow Me

Page 18
Who Will Win the Race?

Features

Safari Power	Find the words	**Page 10**
Poetry Corner	Grump, Grump, Grump	**Page 11**
	I Can Jump	**Page 23**
readingsafari.com	Safari web site	**Page 24**

She can swing.

He can jump.

She can jump.

He can run,

and he can swing,

and he can jump.

Safari WORD POWER

 Aa
 Zz

 Bb
 Yy

 Cc
 Xx

Dd
 Ww

Ee
 Vv

 Ff
 Uu

 Gg
 Tt

 Hh
 Ss

 Ii
 Rr

Find –
can He I jump Jump run
She the too will

 Jj Kk Ll Mm Nn Oo Pp Qq

10

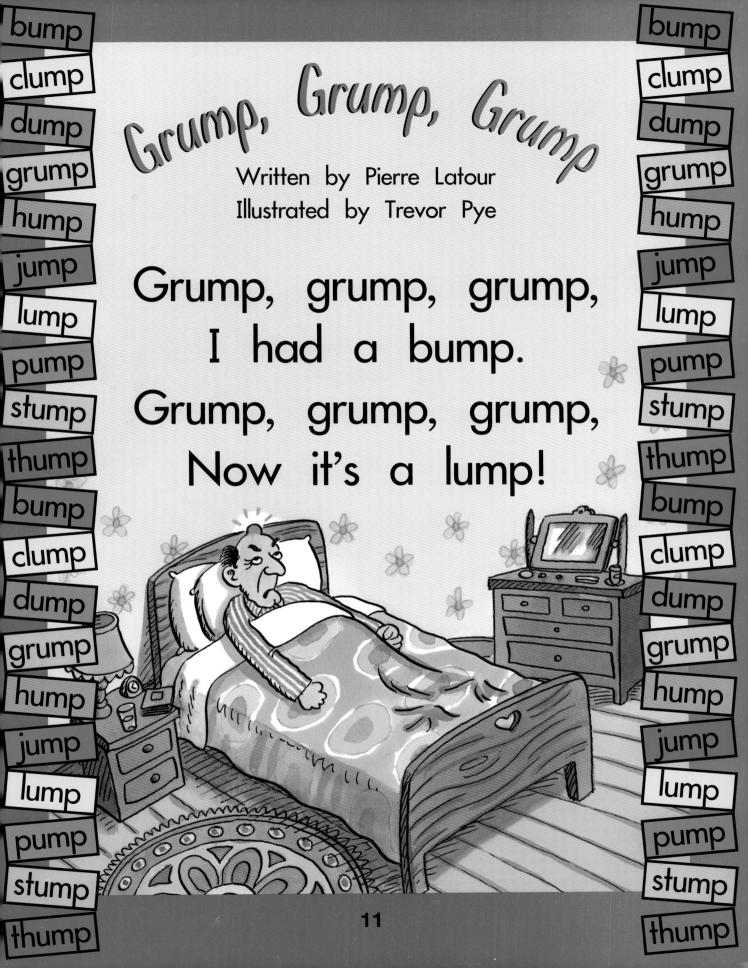

Grump, Grump, Grump

Written by Pierre Latour
Illustrated by Trevor Pye

Grump, grump, grump,
I had a bump.
Grump, grump, grump,
Now it's a lump!

bump
clump
dump
grump
hump
jump
lump
pump
stump
thump
bump
clump
dump
grump
hump
jump
lump
pump
stump
thump

Follow Me

Written by Jade Michaels

Illustrated by Fraser Williamson

I can run.

I can run, too.

I can jump.

I can jump, too.

I can swing.

I can swing, too.

Who Will Win the Race?

Written by Josephine Selwyn
Illustrated by Martin Bailey

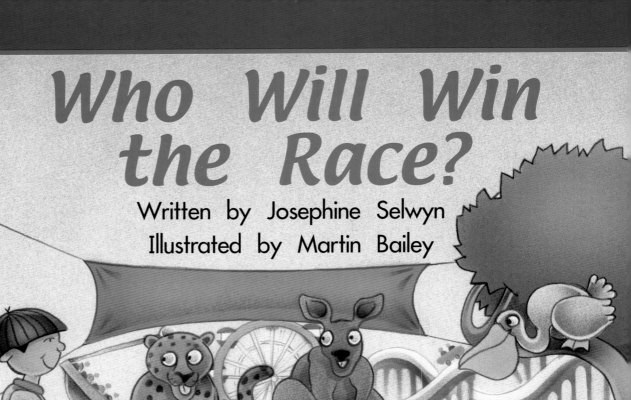

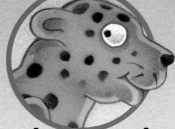

Alligator

Bird

Boy

Cheetah

Kangaroo

Boy

Who will win the race?

 Bird

I will win the race.

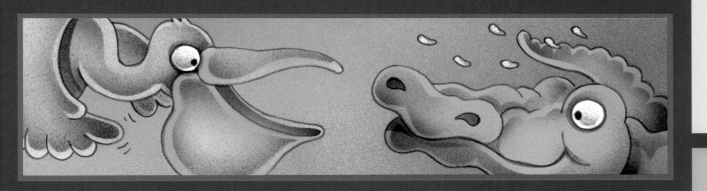

 Alligator

I will win the race.

Kangaroo

I will win the race.

 Cheetah

I will win the race.

Boy
Go!

 Bird
Fly, fly, fly.

 Alligator
Swim, swim, swim.

Kangaroo
Jump, jump, jump.

 Cheetah
Run, run, run.

 Boy
Cheetah wins the race!

I Can Jump

Written by Michele Ashley
Illustrated by Jenny Cooper

I can jump.
Jump, jump, jump.
Over the lump.
Jump, jump, jump.

I can jump
Over the lump.
Jump, jump, jump,
Bump, bump, bump!

readingsafari.com

Check out these Safari magazines, too!

Have your say -

e-mail your Safari Tour Guide at
tourguide@readingsafari.com

 40

Safari Tour Guide,

I won a race.
Shall I tell you about it?

Michael Mendoza (6)

Find some fun things to do!

Go to –
http://www.readingsafari.com

Safari *Superstar*

Name – Mother Monkey

Birthday – June 12

Find out more about this
Safari Superstar at
http://www.readingsafari.com